Foreword

The safety of bulk carriers is one of the most important issues that IMO has addressed in recent years and, as a result, a number of safety measures, covering both structural and operational aspects of such ships, have been recently introduced by the Organization. The Code of Practice for the Safe Loading and Unloading of Bulk Carriers (BLU Code) is one such measure.

Being concerned about the continued loss of ships carrying solid bulk cargoes, sometimes without a trace, and the heavy loss of life incurred, and recognizing that a number of accidents have occurred as a result of improper loading and unloading of bulk carriers, the Sub-Committee on Dangerous Goods, Solid Cargoes and Containers (DSC) at its first session (February 1996) developed a draft code of practice for the safe loading and unloading of bulk carriers, with the aim of preventing such accidents.

The Code was reviewed by the Maritime Safety Committee (MSC) at its sixty-sixth session (June 1996) and by the DSC at its second session (February 1997), and was subsequently approved by the MSC at its sixty-eighth session (June 1997); finally, it was adopted by the Assembly at its twentieth session (November 1997) by resolution A.862(20).

In adopting the resolution, the Assembly urged Governments to implement the BLU Code at the earliest possible opportunity, and to inform IMO of any non-compliance. It further urged Governments in whose territories solid bulk cargo loading and unloading terminals are situated to introduce port by-laws as follows:

- terminal operators are required to comply with the relevant IMO codes and recommendations on ship/port co-operation.

- terminal operators are required to appoint a "terminal representative" as stipulated in section 1.6 of the annex to resolution A.797(19);

- the master is responsible at all times for the safe loading and un-loading of the ship, the details of which should be confirmed with the terminal operator in the form of an agreed loading or unloading plan;

- in case of non-compliance with the agreed loading or unloading plans or any other situation which endangers the safety of the ship, the master has the right to stop the loading or unloading; and

- port authorities have the right to stop the loading or unloading of solid bulk cargoes when the safety of the ship carrying such cargoes is endangered.

The BLU Code, which provides guidance to ship masters of bulk carriers, terminal operators and other parties concerned for the safe handling, loading and unloading of solid bulk cargoes, is also linked to regulation VI/7 (Loading, unloading and stowage of bulk cargoes) of the 1974 SOLAS Convention, as amended by resolution MSC.47(66).

Contents

Code of Practice for the Safe Loading and Unloading of Bulk Carriers

Introduction

1   This Code of Practice for the Safe Loading and Unloading of Bulk Carriers* has been developed by the International Maritime Organization to minimize losses of bulk carriers.

2   The purpose of the Code is to assist persons responsible for the safe loading or unloading of bulk carriers to carry out their functions and to promote the safety of bulk carriers.

3   The Code primarily covers the safety of ships loading and unloading solid bulk cargoes, excluding grain, and reflects current issues, best practices and legislative requirements. Broader safety and pollution issues such as those covered by the SOLAS, MARPOL and Load Line Conventions are not specifically included in the Code.

4   The recommendations in this Code provide guidance to ship-owners, masters, shippers, operators of bulk carriers, charterers and terminal operators for the safe handling, loading, and unloading of solid bulk cargoes. The recommendations are subject to terminal and port requirements, or national regulations. Persons responsible for the loading or unloading of bulk carriers should also be aware of such regulations and requirements.

5   Masters and terminals loading and unloading solid bulk cargoes possessing chemical hazards should also refer to SOLAS chapters II-2 and VII and to MSC/Circ.675 (Recommendations on the safe transport of dangerous cargoes and related activities in port areas).

6   The requirements of individual terminals and port authorities should be published in terminal and port information books. The type of information usually given in these books is listed in appendix 1. The books should be given to the masters of ships where possible before or on arrival at a port or terminal.

---

* The Code of Safe Practice for the Safe Loading and Unloading of Bulk Carriers comprises the annex to resolution A.862(20), the text of which is given at the end of this publication.

7   It is recommended that a copy of this Code be made available to every ship, charterer and bulk loading or unloading terminal so that advice on operational procedures is readily available and respective responsibilities are identified.

Section 1
Definitions

For the purpose of the Code the following definitions apply:

1.1   *Air draught* means the vertical distance from the surface of the water to the highest point of mast or aerial.

1.2   *Combination carriers (OBO or O/O)* means a ship whose design is similar to a conventional bulk carrier but is equipped with pipelines, pumps and inert gas plant so as to enable the carriage of oil cargoes in designated spaces.

1.3   *Conveyor system* means the entire system for delivering cargo from the shore stockpile or receiving point to the ship.

1.4   *Hot work* means the use of open fires and flames, power tools or hot rivets, grinding, soldering, burning, cutting, welding or any other repair work involving heat or creating sparks which may lead to a hazard because of the presence or proximity of flammable atmosphere.

1.5   *List indication lights* means lights, visible from the deck, which light up to show that a ship is listing.

1.6   *Master* means the master of the ship or a ship's officer designated by the master.

1.7   *Pour* means the quantity of cargo poured through one hatch opening as one step in the loading plan, i.e. from the time the spout is positioned over a hatch opening until it is moved to another hatch opening.

1.8   *Terminal representative* means a person appointed by the terminal or other facility where the ship is loading or unloading, who has responsibility for operations conducted by that terminal or facility with regard to the particular ship.

1.9   *Trimming* (loading cargo) is the partial or total levelling of the cargo within the holds, by means of loading spouts or chutes, portable machinery, equipment or manual labour.

1.10 *Trimming* (unloading cargo) is the shovelling or sweeping up of smaller quantities of the cargo in the holds by mechanical means (such as bulldozers) or other means to place them in a convenient position for discharge.

1.11 *Trimming* (ship) is the adding, removal or shifting of weight in a ship to achieve the required forward and aft draughts.

Section 2
Suitability of ships and terminals

2.1 General

2.1.1 All ships nominated for loading should hold the appropriate valid statutory certification including, if required, the document of compliance* for ships carrying solid dangerous goods in bulk. It is recommended that the period of validity of the ship's certificates be sufficient to remain valid during loading, voyage and unloading times, plus a reserve to allow for delays in berthing, inclement weather or both.

2.1.2 The shipowner, manager or operator, when offering a ship for a particular cargo or service, should ensure that the ship:

.1 is maintained in a sound, seaworthy condition;

.2 has on board a competent crew;

.3 has on board at least one officer proficient in the languages used at both the loading and unloading ports, or has an officer available who is proficient in the English language; and

.4 is free of defects that may prejudice the ship's safe navigation, loading or unloading.

2.1.3 It is essential that a ship selected to transport a solid bulk cargo be suitable for its intended purpose taking into account the terminals at which it will load or unload.

2.1.4 The charterer and shipper when accepting a ship for a particular cargo or service should ensure that the ship:

.1 is suitable for access to the planned loading or unloading facilities; and

.2 does not have cargo handling equipment which would inhibit the safety of the loading and unloading operations.

---

* Applicable to ships constructed on or after 1 September 1984.

2.2 Ships

2.2.1 Ships nominated for bulk loading should be suitable for the intended cargo. Suitable ships should be:

.1 weathertight, and efficient in all respects for the normal perils of the sea and the intended voyage;

.2 provided with an approved stability and loading booklet written in a language understood by the ship's officers concerned and using standard expressions and abbreviations. If the language is neither English, nor French, nor Spanish, a translation into one of these languages should be included;

.3 provided with hatch openings of sufficient size to enable the cargo to be loaded, stowed and unloaded satisfactorily; and

.4 provided with the hatch identification numbers used in the loading manual and loading or unloading plan. The location, size and colour of these numbers should be chosen so that they are clearly visible to the operator of the loading or unloading equipment.

2.2.2 It is recommended that all ships which are required to carry out stress calculations should have on board an approved loading instrument for the rapid calculation of such stresses.

2.2.3 All propulsion and auxiliary machinery should be in good functional order. Deck equipment related to mooring and berthing operations, including anchors, cables, mooring lines, hawsers and winches, should be operable and in good order and condition.

2.2.4 All hatches, hatch operating systems and safety devices should be in good functional order, and used only for their intended purpose.

2.2.5 List indication lights, if fitted, should be tested prior to loading or unloading and proved operational.

2.2.6 Ship's own cargo handling equipment should be properly certificated and maintained, and used only under the general supervision of suitably qualified ship's personnel.

2.3 Terminals

2.3.1 Terminal operators should ensure that they only accept ships that can safely berth alongside their installation, taking into consideration issues such as:

.1 water depth at the berth;

.2 maximum size of the ship;

.3   mooring arrangements;

.4   fendering;

.5   safe access; and

.6   obstructions to loading/unloading operations.

2.3.2   Terminal equipment should be properly certificated and maintained in accordance with the relevant national regulations and/or standards, and only operated by duly qualified and, if appropriate, certificated personnel.

2.3.2.1   Where automatic weighing equipment is provided, this should be calibrated at regular intervals.

2.3.3   Terminal personnel should be trained in all aspects of safe loading and unloading of bulk carriers, commensurate with their responsibilities.

2.3.3.1   The training should be designed to provide familiarity with the general hazards of loading, unloading and carriage of bulk cargoes and the adverse effect improper cargo handling operations may have on the safety of the ship.

2.3.4   Terminal operators should ensure that personnel involved in the loading and unloading operations are duly rested to avoid fatigue.

Section 3
Procedures between ship and shore prior to the ship's arrival

3.1   Information exchange: general

3.1.1   It is important that the ship be provided with information about a terminal so the loading or unloading can be planned. Similarly, the terminal will need information about the ship to enable preparations to be made to load or unload the ship. It is important that the information be exchanged in sufficient time to allow preparations to be made.

3.1.2   Before loading commences there should be an agreement between the master and the terminal representative as to the rate of loading and order in which the cargo is to be distributed so as to achieve the final loading plan. In general, this agreement should be based on one or more of the following options:

    .1   the limitations or restrictions on loading procedures, if such are specified in the ship's loading manual or trim and stability booklet, or both;

.2 if the restrictions mentioned in .1 do not exist, and the ship has a loading instrument which has been approved, the loading plan should be prepared on the instrument and there should be a protocol in place so that the loading remains, at all times, within the approved stress limits of the ship; and/or

.3 if neither .1 or .2 can be satisfied, then a conservative procedure should be followed.

3.1.3 Details should be provided of any necessary repairs which may delay berthing, the commencement of loading or unloading, or may delay the ship sailing on completion of loading or unloading.

3.1.4 The master should ensure he receives from the shipper of the intended cargo details of the nature of the cargo required by chapter VI of SOLAS 1974, as amended.* Where additional details, such as trimming or continuous measurement of the water in the cargo, etc., are required, the master should inform the terminal accordingly.

3.2   Information given by the ship to the terminal

3.2.1 In order to plan the proper disposition and availability of the cargo so as to meet the ship's loading plan, the loading terminal should be given the following information:

.1 The ship's estimated time of arrival (ETA) off the port as early as possible. This advice should be updated as appropriate.

.2 At the time of initial ETA advice, the ship should also provide details of the following:

.2.1 name, call sign, IMO Number of the ship, its flag State and port of registry;

.2.2 a loading plan stating the quantity of cargo required, stowage by hatches, loading order and the quantity to be loaded in each pour, provided the ship has sufficient information to be able to prepare such a plan;

.2.3 arrival and proposed departure draughts;

.2.4 time required for deballasting;

.2.5 the ship's length overall, beam, and length of the cargo area from the forward coaming of the forwardmost hatch to the after coaming of the aftmost hatch into which cargo is to be loaded or from which cargo is to be removed;

---

* Refer to MSC/Circ.663 and to the form for cargo information, which is set out in appendix 5.

.2.6 distance from the waterline to the first hatch to be loaded or unloaded and the distance from the ship's side to the hatch opening;

.2.7 the location of the ship's accommodation ladder;

.2.8 air draught;

.2.9 details and capacities of ship's cargo handling gear;

.2.10 number and type of mooring lines; and

.2.11 any other item related to the ship requested by the terminal.

.3 Similar information in respect of ETA, unloading plan and details of the ship are required by unloading terminals.

3.2.2 Ships arriving at loading or unloading terminals in a part-loaded condition should also advise:

.1 berthing displacement and draughts;

.2 previous loading or unloading port;

.3 nature and stowage of cargo already on board and, when dangerous goods in bulk are on board, the name of the material, IMO Class and UN Number or BC Number.

.4 distribution of cargo on board, indicating that to be unloaded and that to remain on board.

3.2.3 Combination carriers (OBO or O/O) should advise of the following additional information:

.1 nature of the preceding three cargoes;

.2 date and place at which the last oil cargo was discharged;

.3 advice as to content of slop tanks and whether fully inerted and sealed; and

.4 date, place and name of authority that issued the last gas free certificate which includes pipelines and pumps.*

3.2.4 As soon as possible the ship should confirm that all holds into which cargo is to be loaded are clean, and free from previous cargo residues which in combination with the cargo to be loaded could create a hazard.

3.2.5 Information on the loading or unloading plan and on intended arrival and departure draughts should be progressively updated, and passed to the terminal as circumstances change.

---

* Refer to the chapter for combination carriers in the *International Safety Guide for Oil Tankers and Terminals (ISGOTT)* and in particular to the section on cargo change-over checklists and the section on discharge of bulk cargo.

3.3 Information given by the terminal to the ship

3.3.1 On receipt of the ship's initial notification of its ETA, the terminal should give the ship the following information as soon as possible:

- **.1** the name of the berth at which loading or unloading will take place and the estimated times for berthing and completion of loading or unloading;

- **.2** characteristics of the loading or unloading equipment, including the terminal's nominal loading or unloading rate and the number of loading or unloading heads to be used;

- **.3** features of the berth or jetty the master may need to be aware of, including the position of fixed and mobile obstructions, fenders, bollards and mooring arrangements;

- **.4** minimum depth of water alongside the berth and in approach or departure channels;

- **.5** water density at the berth;

- **.6** the maximum distance between the waterline and the top of cargo hatch covers or coamings, whichever is relevant to the loading operation, and the maximum air draught;

- **.7** arrangements for gangways and access;

- **.8** which side of the ship is to be alongside the berth;

- **.9** maximum allowable speed of approach to the jetty and availability of tugs, their type and bollard pull;

- **.10** the loading sequence for different parcels of cargo, and any other restrictions if it is not possible to take the cargo in any order or any hold to suit the ship;

- **.11** any properties of the cargo to be loaded which may present a hazard when placed in contact with cargo or residues on board;

- **.12** advance information on the proposed cargo handling operations or changes to existing plans for cargo handling;

- **.13** if the terminal's loading or unloading equipment is fixed, or has any limits to its movement;

- **.14** mooring lines required;

- **.15** warning of unusual mooring arrangements;

- **.16** any restrictions on deballasting;

- **.17** maximum sailing draught permitted by the port authority; and

- **.18** any other items related to the terminal requested by the master.

3.3.2   Information on estimated times for berthing and departure and on minimum water depth at the berth should be progressively updated and passed to the master on receipt of successive ETA advices.

3.3.3   The terminal representative should be satisfied that the ship has been advised as early as possible of the information contained in the cargo declaration as required by chapter VI of SOLAS 1974, as amended.

Section 4
Procedures between the ship and terminal prior to cargo handling

4.1   Principles

4.1.1   The master is responsible at all times for the safe loading and unloading of the ship, the details of which should be confirmed to the terminal representative in the form of a loading or unloading plan. In addition, the master should:

.1   ensure that the checklist in appendix 3 is completed in consultation with the terminal before loading or unloading is commenced;

.2   ensure that the loading or unloading of cargo and the discharge or intake of ballast water is under the control of the ship's officer in charge;

.3   ensure that the disposition of cargo and ballast water is monitored throughout the loading or unloading process to ensure that the ship's structure is not overstressed;

.4   ensure that the terminal representative is made aware of the requirements for harmonization between deballasting and cargo loading rates for his ship;

.5   ensure that ballast water is discharged at rates which conform to the agreed loading plan and do not result in flooding of the quay or of adjacent craft;

.6   retain on board sufficient officers and crew to attend to the adjustment of mooring lines or for any normal or emergency situation, having regard to the need of the crew to have sufficient rest periods to avoid fatigue;

.7   ensure the loading or unloading plans have been passed to and agreed with the terminal representative;

.8   ensure that the terminal representative is made aware of the cargo trimming requirements;

.9 ensure that appropriate information about the cargo to be loaded (appendix 5) has been received to enable safe stowage and carriage to be achieved;

.10 ensure that there is agreement between ship and shore as to the action to be taken in the event of rain, or other change in the weather, when the nature of the cargo would pose a hazard in the event of such a change; and

.11 ensure that no hot work is carried out on board the ship while the ship is alongside the berth except with the permission of the terminal representative and in accordance with any requirements of the port administration.

4.1.2 The terminal representative is responsible for loading or unloading cargo in accordance with the hatch sequence and tonnages stated on the ship's loading or unloading plan. In addition, the terminal representative should:

.1 complete the checklist in appendix 3 in consultation with the master before loading or unloading is commenced;

.2 not deviate from the loading or unloading plan unless by prior consultation and agreement with the master;

.3 trim the cargo, when loading or unloading, to the master's requirements;

.4 maintain a record of the weight and disposition of the cargo loaded or unloaded and ensure that the weights in the hold do not deviate from the plan;

.5 provide the master with the names and procedures for contacting the terminal personnel or shipper's agent who will have responsibility for the loading or unloading operation and with whom the master will have contact;

.6 avoid damage to the ship by the loading or unloading equipment and inform the master, if damage occurs;

.7 ensure that no hot work is carried out on board or in the vicinity of the ship while the ship is alongside the berth except with the permission of the master and in accordance with any requirements of the port administration; and

.8 ensure that there is agreement between the master and the terminal representative at all stages and in relation to all aspects of the loading or unloading operation.

4.2 Procedures

4.2.1 The following are considered important procedures in respect of cargo loading:

.1 the master and terminal representative should indicate agreement to the loading plan before commencement of loading by signing the plan in the spaces provided;

.2 the master should state on the agreed loading plan, the order in which the holds are to be loaded, the weight of each pour, the total weight in each hold and the amount of cargo for vessel trimming purposes, if required;

.3 the terminal representative, on receipt of the ship's initial loading plan (see 3.2.1), should advise the master of the nominal loading rate at which the ship may expect to receive the cargo and the estimated time required to complete each pour;

.4 where it is not practical for the ship to completely discharge its ballast water prior to reaching the trimming stage in the loading process, the master and the terminal representative should agree on the times at which loading may need to be suspended and the duration of such suspensions;

.5 the loading plan should be prepared so as to ensure that all ballast pumping rates and loading rates are considered carefully to avoid overstressing the hull;

.6 the quantities of cargo required to achieve the departure draft and trim should allow for all cargo on the terminal's conveyor systems to be run off and empty on completion of a loading. The terminal representative should advise the master of the nominal tonnage contained on its conveyor system and any requirements for clearing the conveyor system on completion of loading; and

.7 communication arrangements between the ship and terminal should be capable of responding to requests for information on the loading process and of prompt compliance in the event that the master or terminal representative orders loading to be suspended. Consideration should be given to the disposition of cargo on the conveyor systems and to the response time in the event of an emergency stop.

4.2.2 The following are considered important procedures in respect of cargo unloading:

.1 the terminal representative, when proposing or accepting the initial unloading plan, should advise the master of the nominal unloading rate and the estimated time required for each stage of the discharge;

.2 the master should advise the hold order and the weight to be unloaded in each stage of the discharge;

11

    .3   the terminal representative should give the ship the maximum warning when it is intended to increase, or to reduce, the number of unloading heads used; and

    .4   communication arrangements between ship and terminal should be capable of responding to requests for information on the unloading process, and of prompt compliance in the event that the master orders unloading to be suspended.

4.3   Implementation

4.3.1   The loading or unloading plan should be prepared in a form such as that shown in appendix 2. Worked examples of this form are also shown in appendix 2. A different form may be used provided it contains the essential information to meet the requirements of this Code. The minimum information for this purpose is that enclosed in the heavy line box on the sample form.

4.3.2   The loading or unloading plan should only be changed when a revised plan has been prepared, accepted and signed by both parties. Loading plans should be kept by the ship and terminal for a period of six months.

4.3.3   A copy of the agreed loading or unloading plan and any subsequent amendments to it should be lodged with the appropriate authority of the port State.

Section 5
Cargo loading and handling of ballast

5.1   General

5.1.1   When the cargo loading plan is agreed, the master and terminal representative should confirm the method of cargo operations so as to ensure no excessive stresses on the hull, tank top and associated structures, and exchange information to avoid any structural damage to the ship by cargo handling equipment.

5.1.2   The terminal representative should alert the master, when the cargo is heavy, or when the individual grab loads are large, that there may be high, localized impact loads on the ship's structure until the tank top is completely covered by cargo, especially when high free-fall drops are permitted. As such impacts have the potential for causing structural damage, special care should be taken at the start of the loading operation in each cargo hold.

5.1.3 Monitoring of the cargo handling operation, and effective communication between the terminal and ship, must be maintained at all times, and especially during final trimming of the ship.

5.1.4 Any requirement for cargo trimming should be in accordance with the procedures of the IMO Code of Safe Practice for Solid Bulk Cargoes (BC Code).

5.1.5 In order to effectively monitor the progress of the cargo loading operation it is essential for both the master and terminal representative to have readily accessible information on the total quantity loaded, as well as the quantities per pour.

5.1.6 On completion of loading, the master and the terminal representative should agree in writing that the ship has been loaded in accordance with the loading plan, including any agreed variations.

5.2   Ship duties

5.2.1 The master should advise the terminal representative of any deviation from the deballasting plan or any other matter which may affect cargo loading.

5.2.2 The ship should be kept upright or, if a list is required for operational reasons, it should be kept as small as possible.

5.2.3 The master should ensure close supervision of the loading operation and of the ship during final stages of loading. The master should advise the terminal representative when final trimming of the ship has to commence in order to allow for the conveyor system run-off.

5.3   Terminal duties

5.3.1 The terminal representative should advise the master on any change to the agreed loading rate and, at the completion of each pour, the terminal representative should advise the master of the weight loaded and that cargo loading continues in accordance with the agreed cargo plan.

5.3.2 The ship should be kept upright with the cargo distributed so as to eliminate any twisting of the ship's structure.

5.3.3 The terminal should use weight meters which are well maintained and provide an accuracy to within 1% of the rated quantity required over the normal range of loading rates. The terminal should frequently monitor the weight of cargo that is being loaded and inform the ship so that it can be compared with the cargo loading plan and the ship's calculation by draught marks.

Section 6
Unloading cargo and handling of ballast

6.1 General

6.1.1 When the cargo unloading plan is agreed, the master and terminal representative must confirm the method of cargo operations so as to ensure no excessive stresses on the hull, tank top and associated structures, including any measures to reduce and eliminate any structural damage to the ship by cargo handling equipment.

6.1.2 Monitoring and effective communication between the terminal and ship must be maintained at all times.

6.1.3 On completion of unloading, the master and the terminal representative should agree in writing that the ship has been unloaded in accordance with the agreed unloading plan, with the holds emptied and cleaned to the master's requirements, and should record any detected damage suffered by the ship.

6.1.4 In order to maintain an effective monitoring of the progress of the cargo unloading plan, it is essential for both the master and the terminal representative to have readily accessible information on the total unloaded quantity as well as on the quantities unloaded per hatch.

6.1.5 When ballasting one or more holds, master and terminal operator should take account of the possibility of the discharge of flammable vapours from the holds. Suitable precautions* should be taken before any hot work is permitted adjacent to or above that space.

6.2 Ship duties

6.2.1 The master will advise the terminal representative of any deviation from the ballasting plan or any other matter which may effect cargo unloading.

6.2.2 At the start and during all stages of unloading cargo, the master should ensure that frequent checks are made so that:

    .1   cargo spaces and other enclosed spaces are well ventilated, and persons are allowed to enter them only after they have been declared safe for entry in accordance with the guidelines[†] developed by the Organization;

---

* Refer to the section on the operation of combination carriers in the *International Safety Guide for Oil Tankers and Terminals (ISGOTT)*.

[†] Refer to Assembly resolution A.864(20), Recommendations for entering enclosed spaces aboard ships.

.2　the cargo is being unloaded from each hold in accordance with the agreed unloading plan;

.3　the ballasting operation is proceeding in accordance with the agreed unloading plan;

.4　the ship is securely moored, and that weather conditions are being monitored and local weather forecasts obtained;

.5　the ship's draught is read regularly to monitor the progress of the unloading;

.6　the terminal representative is warned immediately if the unloading process has caused damage, has created a hazardous situation, or is likely to do so;

.7　the ship is kept upright, or, if a list is required for operational reasons, it is kept as small as possible; and

.8　the unloading of the port side closely matches that of the starboard side in the same hold to avoid twisting the ship.

6.2.3　The master should ensure close supervision of the final stages of the unloading, to ensure that all cargo is unloaded.

6.3　Terminal duties

6.3.1　The terminal representative should follow the agreed unloading plan and should consult with the master if there is a need to amend the plan.

6.3.2　The ship is to be kept upright or, if a list is required for operational reasons, it is to be kept as small as possible.

6.3.3　The unloading of the port side should closely match that of the starboard side in the same hold, to avoid twisting the ship.

6.3.4　Unloading rates and sequences should not be altered by the terminal unless by prior consultation and agreement between the master and the terminal representative.

6.3.5　The terminal representative should advise the master when unloading is considered to be completed from each hold.

6.3.6　The terminal should make every effort to avoid damage to the ship when using unloading or hold cleaning equipment. If damage does occur, it should be reported to the master and, if necessary, repaired. If the damage could impair the structural capability or watertight integrity of the hull, or the ship's essential engineering systems, the Administration or an organization recognized by it and the appropriate authority of the port State should be informed, so that they can decide whether immediate repair is necessary or whether it can be deferred. In either case, the action taken, whether to carry out the repair or defer it, should be to the satisfaction of the Administration or an organization recognized by it and the appropriate authority of the port State. Where immediate repair is considered necessary, it should be carried out to the satisfaction of the master before the ship leaves the port.

6.3.7 The terminal representative should monitor the weather conditions and provide the master with the forecast of any local adverse weather condition.

Appendix 1
Recommended contents of port and terminal information books

1   It is recommended that information books prepared by terminal operators, port authorities or both should contain the following information relating to their site-specific requirements:

1.1   Port information books:

.1   location of the port and the terminal

.2   details of port administration

.3   radiocommunication procedures and frequencies

.4   arrival information requirements

.5   port health, immigration, quarantine and customs regulations and procedures

.6   relevant charts and nautical publications

.7   pilotage requirements

.8   towage and tug assistance

.9   berthing and anchorage facilities

.10   port emergency procedures

.11   significant weather features

.12   availability of fresh water, provisions, bunkers and lubricants

.13   the maximum size of ship the port can accept

.14   maximum permissible draught and minimum depth of water in navigation channels

.15   water density at the port

.16   maximum permissible air draught

.17   requirements for ship's draught and trim for navigation in the waterways

.18   tidal and current information, as it affects ship movements

.19   restrictions or conditions on the discharge of ballast water

.20   statutory requirements regarding loading and cargo declaration

.21   information on waste reception facilities in the port

1.2   Terminal information books:

.1   details of terminal contact personnel

.2   technical data on the berths and loading or unloading equipment

.3   depth of water at the berth

.4   water density at the berth

.5   the minimum and maximum size of ship which the terminal's facilities are designed to accept, including the minimum clearance between deck obstructions

.6   mooring arrangements and attendance of mooring lines

.7   loading or unloading rates and equipment clearances

.8   loading or unloading procedures and communications

.9   cargo weight determinations by weightmeter and draught survey

.10   conditions for acceptance of combination carriers

.11   access to and from ships and berths or jetties

.12   terminal emergency procedures

.13   damage and indemnity arrangements

.14   landing location of accommodation ladder

.15   information on waste reception facilities at the terminal

1.3   Extreme cold weather information

Ports and terminals situated in regions subject to extreme cold weather should advise masters where to obtain information on operation of ships under such conditions.

Appendix 2
Loading or unloading plan

97525

Example Loading/Unloading Plan The loading or unloading plan should be prepared in a form such as shown below. Worked examples of this form are shown overleaf. A different form may be used provided it contains the essential information enclosed in the heavy line box.

LOADING OR UNLOADING PLAN Version No	Date	Vessel			Voyage No
Load/Unload Port	Cargo(es)	Assumed stowage factor of cargo(es)	Ballast pumping rate	Dock water density	Max draught available (HW)	Max air draught in berth
To/from Port	Last cargo	No. of loaders/ dischargers	Load/ discharge rate		Min draught available (LW)	Max sailing/ arrival draught

Tonnes											
Grade	11	10	9	8	7	6	5	4	3	2	1
Totals:	Grade	Tonnes	Grade	Tonnes	Grade	Tonnes	Grade	Tonnes	Total:	Tonnes

Pour No.	Cargo		Ballast operations	Time required (hours)	Comments	Calculated values							Calculated values				Observed Values		
	Hold No.	Tonnes				Draught		Maximum			Air draught	Draught mid	Trim		Draught		Draught	
						Fwd	Aft	BM*	SF*					Fwd	Aft	Mid	Fwd	Aft	Mid

| TOTAL | | | | |

Signed Terminal

Signed Ship

NO DEVIATION FROM ABOVE PLAN WITHOUT PRIOR APPROVAL OF CHIEF MATE
Pours to be numbered 1A, 1B, 2*, 2B, etc when using two loaders
Abbreviations: PI = Pump In GI = Gravitate In F = Full PO = Pump Out GO = Gravitate Out MT = Empty
All entries within the box must be completed as far as possible. The entries outside the box are optional.

*Bending moments (BM) & shear forces (SF) are to be expressed as a percentage of maximum permitted in-port values for intermediate stages, and of maximum permitted at-sea values for the final stage. Every step in the loading/unloading plan must remain within the allowable limits for hull girder shear forces, bending moments and tonnage per hold, where applicable. Loading/unloading operations may have to be paused to allow for ballasting/ deballasting in order to keep actual values within limits.

19

Worked examples

Example Loading/Unloading Plan

The loading or unloading plan should be prepared in a form such as shown below. A different form may be used provided it contains the essential information enclosed in the heavy line box.

LOADING OR UNLOADING PLAN Version No.	1	Date	96-03-24
Vessel	BARBICAN	Voyage No.	044
Load/Unload Port	BOCA GRANDE	Cargo(es)	IRON ORE
Assumed stowage factor of cargo(es)	FINES/LUMP	Dock water density	1.025
Max draught available (HW)	17.88 m	Max air draught in berth	N/A
To/From Port	JAPAN F.O.	Last cargo	IRON ORE & COAL
No. of loaders/dischargers	1	Ballast pumping rate	4000 t/hr
Load/discharge rate	4500 t/hr	Min draught available (LW)	9.62 m
Max sailing/arrival draught	17.88 m		

Tonnes / Grade: FINES = 44706 Tonnes; LUMP = 98294 Tonnes

Tonnes	914756	817000	717382	516382	315382	215766	113050
Grade	FINES	LUMP	LUMP	LUMP	LUMP	LUMP	FINES/LUMP

						Calculated values — Draught		Maximum				
Pour No.	Hold No.	Tonnes	Ballast operations	Time required (hours)	Comments	Fwd	Aft	BM*	SF*	Air draught	Draught mid	Trim
1	4	10000	GO 1&3 UWT's	2.22	FINES	9.99	10.77	73	49		10.38	0.78
2	1	7000	GO Upper Fore Peak PO 2 Hold	1.56	FINES changeover 2 Hold	10.16	10.43	66	53		10.31	0.34
3	9	8000	GO 5 UWT's PO Aft peak	1.78	FINES	9.42	12.15	63	59		10.79	2.73
4	5	6900	PO 1DB's	1.53	FINES	10.12	12.50	80	43		11.31	2.38
5	9	6756	PO 5 DB's	1.50	FINES	9.56	13.76	80	45		11.65	4.18
6	1	6050	PO Lower FP GO 2 UWT's	1.36	FINES	9.61	13.57	75	49		11.59	3.96
					Change grade to LUMP							
7	7	10000	GO 6 Hold to 50%	2.22	LUMP	8.94	14.38	-58	55		11.66	5.63
8	5	10000	PO 6 Hold	2.22	LUMP	9.63	13.63	-67	49		11.63	4.00
9	7	7382	Educt 6 Hold	1.64	LUMP changeover 6 Hold	9.57	15.24	-64	47		12.41	5.67
10	3	10000	PO 2&3 DB's	2.22	LUMP	10.41	14.65	-49	38		12.53	4.24
11	8	10000	GO 4 UWT's	2.22	LUMP	9.58	16.66	-50	43		13.12	7.08
12	5	6382	PO 4 DB's	1.42	LUMP	10.28	16.24	58	37		13.26	5.96
13	2	6000	Educt as required	1.33	LUMP	9.90	17.88	53	38		13.89	7.98
14	8	8000	Educt as required	1.78	LUMP	12.51	16.68	-65	46		14.60	4.17
15	6	9000	Educt as required	2.00	LUMP	13.14	17.80	42	-21		15.47	4.66
16	2	6000	Educt as required	1.33	LUMP	15.06	16.98	33	-16		16.02	1.92
17	6	7382	Educt ballast lines	1.64	LUMP	15.99	17.88	48	-30		16.74	2.29
18	3	5382	Shut down ballast	1.20	LUMP	16.95	17.54	44	-27		17.02	0.59
					Trim check							
19	8	1000		0.22	LUMP	16.96	17.72	49	-30		17.33	0.79
20	2	1766		0.39	LUMP	17.51	17.51	46	-27		17.51	0.00
			DRAUGHT SURVEY		SEAGOING CONDITION	17.51	17.51	62	-36		17.51	0.00
TOTAL		143000										

Signed Terminal: [signature]
Signed Ship: A. Smith

NO DEVIATION FROM ABOVE PLAN WITHOUT PRIOR APPROVAL OF CHIEF MATE
Pours to be numbered 1A, 1B, 2A, 2B, etc. when using two loaders
Abbreviations: PI = Pump In G = Gravitate In F = Full PO = Pump Out GO = Gravitate Out MT = Empty
All entries within the box must be completed as far as possible. The entries outside the box are optional.

*Bending moments (BM) & shear forces (SF) are to be expressed as a percentage of maximum permitted. Import values for intermediate stages, and of maximum permitted at-sea values for the final stage. Every step in the loading/unloading plan must remain within the allowable limits for hull girder shear forces, bending moments and tonnage per hold, where applicable. Loading/unloading operations may have to be paused to allow for ballasting/deballasting in order to keep actual values within limits.

Example Loading/Unloading Plan

The loading or unloading plan should be prepared in a form such as shown below. A different form may be used provided it contains the essential information enclosed in the heavy line box.

Loading/Unloading Plan Version No.	1
Date	96-05-15
Vessel	BARBICAN
Voyage No.	044
Load/Unload Port	CHIBA
Cargo(es)	IRON ORE
Max draught available (HW)	17.35m
Max air draught in berth	60m
Dock water density	1.025
To/from Port	BOCA GRANDE
Last cargo	IRON ORE & COAL
Assumed stowage factor of cargo(es)	FINES / LUMP
Ballast pumping rate	6000 t/hr
Min draught available (LW)	7.59m
Max arrival draught	17m
No. of loaders/dischargers	2
Load/discharge rate	1250 t/hr per grab

Tonnes / Grade totals:

Grade	Tonnes
LUMP	215470
FINES	113050
Total	142614

Grade LUMP = 97908 Tonnes Grade FINES = 44706 Tonnes

Pour No.	Hold No.	Cargo Tonnes	Ballast operations	Time required (hours)	Comments	Fwd	Aft	BM*	SF*	Air draught	Draught mid	Trim
1A	2	15670	G1 1&2 DB's P1 2UWT's	13.2	LUMP 2 & 6 Holds MT	13.82	16.29	-72	48			2.67
1B	6	16382										
2A	5	10000	G1 4DB's P1 6 4WT's	9.0	LUMP	13.64	14.54	71	56			1.10
2B	8	10000			LUMP							
3A	7	9000	G1 3DB's	7.2	LUMP	12.19	13.68	77	78			1.69
3B	7	9000										
4A	5	6392	G1 5DB's	5.5	LUMP 5 & 8 Holds MT	12.67	15.22	68	38			2.55
4B	6	6910	P1 6 Hold to 0.5m ullage									
5A	3	6392		6.7	LUMP 3 & 7 Holds MT	11.05	13.96	-91	59			2.89
5B	7	8382										
			Draught survey and change grade to FINES									
6A	1	6000	P1 1&5 4WT's	4.8	FINES	9.75	16.01	83	42			4.26
6B	9	6000										
7A	4	8756		7.0	FINES	9.38	10.64	80	52			1.26
7B	9	8756			FINES							
8A	4	7050	G1 & P1 Lower Forepeak	6.5	FINES	7.59	11.30	84	-82			3.71
8B	4	8166	P1 Upper Forepeak & 3 4WT's		FINES							
			SEAGOING CONDITION			7.59	11.30	84	-82			3.31
TOTAL		142614										

Instructions ① Please empty No 6 Hold and leave as clean as possible. This will then be used for ballast during Stage 6.
② Grab and bulldozer blades must not be allowed to strike the ship's structure. Please instruct drivers to take special care.
③ Please note our bridge and air-draft restrictions in the after camera of each hold. Care required in these areas.
④ All damage to be reported. Holds to be reviewed on cargo completion.

Signed Terminal: DDharma
Signed Ship: A. Smith

NO DEVIATION FROM ABOVE PLAN WITHOUT PRIOR APPROVAL OF CHIEF MATE
Pours to be numbered 1A, 1B, 2A, 2B, etc when using two loaders
Abbreviations: PI = Pump In GI = Gravitate In PO = Pump Out GO = Gravitate Out MT = Empty
All entries within the box must be completed as far as possible. The entries outside the box are optional.

*Bending moments (BM) & shear forces (SF) are to be expressed as a percentage of maximum permitted values. Intermediate stages, and of maximum permitted import values for intermediate stages. Every step in the loading/unloading plan must remain within the allowable limits for hull girder shear forces, bending moments and tonnage per hold, where applicable. Loading/unloading operations may have to be paused to allow for ballasting/deballasting in order to keep actual values within limits.

Appendix 3
Ship/Shore safety checklist
for loading or unloading dry bulk cargo carriers

Date ....

Port.. Terminal/Quay ....

Available depth of water in berth .... Minimum air draught* ....

Ship's name.................................

Arrival draught (read/calculated)................... Air draught ....

Calculated departure draught...................... Air draught ....

The master and terminal manager, or their representatives, should complete the checklist jointly. Advice on points to be considered is given in the accompanying guidelines. The safety of operations requires that all questions should be answered affirmatively and the boxes ticked. If this is not possible, the reason should be given, and agreement reached upon precautions to be taken between ship and terminal. If a question is considered to be not applicable write "N/A", explaining why if appropriate.

		SHIP	**TERMINAL**
1.	Is the depth of water at the berth, and the air draught, adequate for the cargo operations to be completed?	☐	☐
2.	Are mooring arrangements adequate for all local effects of tide, current, weather, traffic and craft alongside?	☐	☐
3.	In emergency, is the ship able to leave the berth at any time?	☐	☐
4.	Is there safe access between the ship and the wharf? *Tended by ship/terminal.*................ (cross out as appropriate)	☐	☐

---

* The term *air draught* should be construed carefully: if the ship is in a river or an estuary, it usually refers to maximum mast height for passing under bridges, while on the berth it usually refers to the height available or required under the loader or unloader.

	SHIP	**TERMINAL**
5. Is the agreed ship/terminal communications system operative? *Communication method* . . . . *Language* . . . . *Radio channels/phone numbers*	☐	☐
6. Are the liaison contact persons during operations positively identified? *Ship contact persons* . . . . *Shore contact person(s)* . . . . *Location*	☐	☐
7. Are adequate crew on board, and adequate staff in the terminal, for emergency?	☐	☐
8. Have any bunkering operations been advised and agreed?	☐	☐
9. Have any intended repairs to wharf or ship whilst alongside been advised and agreed?	☐	☐
10. Has a procedure for reporting and recording damage from cargo operations been agreed?	☐	☐
11. Has the ship been provided with copies of port and terminal regulations, including safety and pollution requirements and details of emergency services?	☐	☐
12. Has the shipper provided the master with the properties of the cargo in accordance with the requirements of chapter VI of SOLAS?	☐	☐
13. Is the atmosphere safe in holds and enclosed spaces to which access may be required, have fumigated cargoes been identified, and has the need for monitoring of atmosphere been agreed by ship and terminal?	☐	☐

	SHIP	TERMINAL

14. Have the cargo handling capacity and any limits of travel for each loader/ unloader been passed to the ship/ terminal?
    Loader ....
    Loader ....
    Loader ....

15. Has a cargo loading or unloading plan been calculated for all stages of loading/ deballasting or unloading/ballasting?
    Copy lodged with ....

16. Have the holds to be worked been clearly identified in the loading or unloading plan, showing the sequence of work, and the grade and tonnage of cargo to be transferred each time the hold is worked?

17. Has the need for trimming of cargo in the holds been discussed, and have the method and extent been agreed?

18. Do both ship and terminal understand and accept that if the ballast programme becomes out of step with the cargo operation, it will be necessary to suspend cargo operation until the ballast operation has caught up?

19. Have the intended procedures for removing cargo residues lodged in the holds while unloading, been explained to the ship and accepted?

20. Have the procedures to adjust the final trim of the loading ship been decided and agreed?
    Tonnage held by the terminal
    conveyor system ....

21. Has the terminal been advised of the time required for the ship to prepare for sea, on completion of cargo work?

THE ABOVE HAS BEEN AGREED:

Time ....   Date ....

For ship ....   For terminal ....

Rank ....   Position/Title ....

Appendix 4
Guidelines for completing
the ship/shore safety checklist

The purpose of the ship/shore safety checklist is to improve working relationships between ship and terminal, and thereby to improve the safety of operations. Misunderstandings occur and mistakes can be made when ships' officers do not understand the intentions of the terminal personnel, and the same applies when terminal personnel do not understand what the ship can and cannot safely do.

Completing the checklist together is intended to help ship and terminal personnel to recognize potential problems, and to be better prepared for them.

1 *Is the depth of water at the berth, and the air draught,* adequate for the cargo operations to be completed?*
The depth of water should be determined over the entire area the ship will occupy, and the terminal should be aware of the ship's maximum air draught and water draught requirements during operations. Where the loaded draught means a small underkeel clearance at departure, the Master should consult and confirm that the proposed departure draught is safe and suitable.

The ship should be provided with all available information about density and contaminates of the water at the berth.

2 *Are mooring arrangements adequate for all local effects of tide, current, weather, traffic and craft alongside?*
Due regard should be given to the need for adequate fendering arrangements. Ships should remain well secured in their moorings. Alongside piers or quays, ranging of the ship should be prevented by keeping mooring lines taut; attention should be given to the movement of the ship caused by tides, currents or passing ships and by the operation in progress.

Wire ropes and fibre ropes should not be used together in the same direction because of differences in their elastic properties.

3 *In emergency, is the ship able to leave the berth at any time?*
The ship should normally be able to move under its own power at short notice, unless agreement to immobilize the ship has been reached with the terminal representative, and the port authority where applicable.

---

* The term *air draught* should be construed carefully: if the ship is in a river or an estuary it usually refers to maximum mast height for passing under bridges, while on the berth it usually refers to the height available or required under the loader or unloaders.

In an emergency a ship may be prevented from leaving the berth at short notice by a number of factors. These include low tide, excessive trim or draught, lack of tugs, no navigation possible at night, main engine immobilized, etc. Both the ship and the terminal should be aware if any of these factors apply, so that extra precautions can be taken if need be.

The method to be used for any emergency unberthing operation should be agreed taking into account the possible risks involved. If emergency towing-off wires are required, agreement should be reached on their position and method of securing.

4   *Is there safe access between the ship and the wharf?*

The means of access between the ship and the wharf must be safe and legal, and may be provided by either ship or terminal. It should consist of an appropriate gangway or accommodation ladder with a properly fastened safety net underneath it. Access equipment must be tended, since it can be damaged as a result of changing heights and draughts; persons responsible for tending it must be agreed between the ship and terminal, and recorded in the checklist.

The gangway should be positioned so that it is not underneath the path of cargo being loaded or unloaded. It should be well illuminated during darkness. A lifebuoy with a heaving line should be available on board the ship near the gangway or accommodation ladder.

5   *Is the agreed ship/terminal communications system operative?*

Communication should be maintained in the most efficient way between the responsible officer on duty on the ship and the responsible person ashore. The selected system of communication and the language to be used, together with the necessary telephone numbers and/or radio channels, should be recorded in the checklist.

6   *Are the liaison contact persons during operations positively identified?*

The controlling personnel on ship and terminal must maintain an effective communication with each other and their respective supervisors. Their names, and if appropriate where they can be contacted, should be recorded in the checklist.

The aim should be to prevent development of hazardous situations, but if such a situation does arise, good communication and knowing who has proper authority can be instrumental in dealing with it.

7   *Are adequate crew on board, and adequate staff in the terminal, for emergency?*

It is not possible or desirable to specify all conditions, but it is important that a sufficient number of personnel should be on board the ship, and in the terminal throughout the ship's stay, to deal with an emergency.

The signals to be used in the event of an emergency arising ashore or on board should be clearly understood by all personnel involved in cargo operations.

8   *Have any bunkering operations been advised and agreed?*

The person on board in charge of bunkering must be identified, together with the time, method of delivery (hose from shore, bunker barge, etc.) and the location of the bunker point on board. Loading of bunkers should be co-ordinated with the cargo operation. The terminal should confirm agreement to the procedure.

9   *Have any intended repairs to wharf or ship whilst alongside*
        been advised and agreed?

Hot work, involving welding, burning or use of naked flame, whether on the ship or the wharf may require a hot work permit. Work on deck which could interfere with cargo work will need to be coordinated.

In the case of combination carrier a gas free certificate (including for pipelines and pumps) will be necessary, issued by a shore chemist approved by the terminal or port authority.

10   *Has a procedure for reporting and recording damage from cargo*
        operations been agreed?

Operational damage can be expected in a harsh trade. To avoid conflict, a procedure must be agreed, before cargo operations commence, to record such damage. An accumulation of small items of damage to steel work can cause significant loss of strength for the ship, so it is essential that damage is noted, to allow prompt repair.

11   *Has the ship been provided with copies of port and terminal regulations,*
        including safety and pollution requirements and details of emergency services?

Although much information will normally be provided by a ship's agent, a fact sheet containing this information should be passed to the ship on arrival, and should include any local regulations controlling the discharge of ballast water and hold washings.

12   *Has the shipper provided the master with the properties of*
        the cargo in accordance with the requirements of chapter VI of SOLAS?

The shipper should pass to the master, for example, the grade of cargo, particle size, quantity to be loaded, stowage factor, and cargo moisture content. The IMO BC Code gives guidance on this.

The ship should be advised of any material which may contaminate or react with the planned cargo, and the ship should ensure that the holds are free of such material.

13   *Is the atmosphere safe in holds and enclosed spaces to which access may be required, have fumigated cargoes been identified, and has the need for monitoring of atmosphere been agreed by ship and terminal?*

Rusting of steelwork or the characteristics of a cargo may cause a hazardous atmosphere to develop. Consideration should be given to: oxygen depletion in holds; the effect of fumigation either of cargo to be discharged, or of cargo in a silo before loading from where gas can be swept on board along with the cargo with no warning to the ship; and leakage of gases, whether poisonous or explosive, from adjacent holds or other spaces.

14   *Have the cargo handling capacity and any limits of travel for each loader/unloader been passed to the ship/terminal?*

The number of loaders or unloaders to be used should be agreed, and their capabilities understood by both parties. The agreed maximum transfer rate for each loader/unloader should be recorded in the checklist.

Limits of travel of loading or unloading equipment should be indicated. This is essential information when planning cargo operations in berths where a ship must be shifted from one position to another due to loading. Gear should always be checked for faults and that it is clear of contaminates from previous cargoes. The accuracy of weighing devices should be ascertained frequently.

15   *Has a cargo loading and unloading plan been calculated for **all** stages of loading/deballasting or unloading/ballasting?*

Where possible the ship should prepare the plan before arrival. To permit her to do so the terminal should provide whatever information the ship requests for planning purposes. On ships which require longitudinal strength calculations, the plan should take account of any permissible maxima for bending moments and shear forces.

The plan should be agreed with the terminal and a copy passed over for use by terminal staff. All watch officers on board and terminal supervisors should have access to a copy. No deviation from the plan should be allowed without agreement of the master.

According to SOLAS regulation VI/7, it is required to lodge a copy of the plan with the appropriate authority of the port State. The person receiving the plan should be recorded in the checklist.

16   *Have the holds to be worked been clearly identified in the loading or unloading plan, showing the sequence of work, and the grade and tonnage of cargo to be transferred each time the hold is worked?*

The necessary information should be provided in the form as set out in appendix 2 of this Code.

17   *Has the need for trimming of cargo in the holds been discussed,*
     and have the method and extent been agreed?

A well-known method is spout trimming, and this can usually achieve a satisfactory result. Other methods use bulldozers, front-end loaders, deflector blades, trimming machines or even manual trimming. The extent of trimming will depend upon the nature of the cargo, and must be in accordance with the BC Code.

18   *Do both ship and terminal understand and accept that if the ballast programme*
     becomes out of step with the cargo operations, it will be necessary to suspend
     cargo operations until the ballast operation has caught up?

All parties will prefer to load or discharge the cargo without stops if possible. However, if the cargo or ballast programmes are out of step a stop to cargo handling must be ordered by the master and accepted by the terminal to avoid the possibility of inadvertently overstressing the ship's structure.

A cargo operations plan will often indicate cargo check points, when conditions will also allow confirmation that the cargo and ballast handling operations are in alignment.

If the maximum rate at which the ship can safely accept the cargo is less than the cargo handling capacity of the terminal, it may be necessary to negotiate pauses in the cargo transfer programme or for the terminal to operate equipment at less than the maximum capacity.

In areas where extremely cold weather is likely, the potential for frozen ballast or ballast lines should be recognized.

19   *Have the intended procedures for removing cargo residues lodged in*
     the holds while unloading been explained to the ship and accepted?

The use of bulldozers, front-end loaders or pneumatic/hydraulic hammers to shake material loose should be undertaken with care, as wrong procedures can damage or distort ships' steel work. Prior agreement to the need and method intended, together with adequate supervision of operators, will avoid subsequent claims or weakening of the ship's structure.

20   *Have the procedures to adjust the final trim of the loading ship*
     been decided and agreed?

Any tonnages proposed at the commencement of loading for adjusting the trim of the ship can only be provisional, and too much importance should not be attached to them. The significance lies in ensuring that the requirement is not overlooked or ignored. The actual quantities and positions to be used to achieve final ship's trim will depend upon the draft readings taken immediately beforehand. The ship should be informed of the tonnage on the conveyor system since that quantity may be large and must still be loaded when the order "stop loading" is given. This figure should be recorded in the checklist.

21   *Has the terminal been advised of the time required for the ship
        to prepare for sea, on completion of cargo work?*

The procedure of securing for sea remains as important as it ever was, and should not be skimped. Hatches should be progressively secured on completion so that only one or two remain to be closed after cargo work is finished.

Modern deep-water terminals for large ships may have very short passages before the open sea is encountered. The time needed to secure, therefore, may vary between day or night, summer or winter, fine weather or foul weather.

Early advice must be given to the terminal if any extension of time is necessary.

Appendix 5
Form for cargo information
(recommended layout)

Note: This form is not applicable if the cargo to be loaded requires a declaration under the requirements of SOLAS 1974, chapter VII, regulation 5; MARPOL 73/78, Annex III, regulation 4; and the IMDG Code, General Introduction section 9.

Shipper		Reference number(s)
Consignee		Carrier
Name/means of transport	Port/place of departure	Instructions or other matters
Port/place of destination		
General description of the cargo (Type of material/particle size)* * For solid bulk cargo		Gross mass (kg/tonnes) ☐ General cargo ☐ Cargo unit(s) ☐ Bulk cargo
Specification of bulk cargo* Stowage factor Angle of repose Trimming procedures Chemical properties† if potential hazard * If applicable † E.g., IMO class, UN No. or BC No. and EmS No.		
Relevant special properties of the cargo		Additional certificate(s)* ☐ Certificate of moisture content and transportable moisture limit ☐ Weathering certificate ☐ Exemption certificate ☐ Other (specify) * If required
DECLARATION I hereby declare that the consignment is fully and accurately described and that the given test results and other specifications are correct to the best of my knowledge and belief and can be considered as representative for the cargo to be loaded.		Name/status, company/organization of signatory Place and date Signature on behalf of shipper

As an aid to paper documentation, Electronic Data Processing (EDP) or Electronic Data Interchange (EDI) techniques may be used.

This form meets the requirements of SOLAS 1974, chapter VI, regulation 2; the BC Code and the CSS Code.

Resolution A.862(20)

adopted on 27 November 1997

Code of Practice for the Safe Loading and Unloading of Bulk Carriers

THE ASSEMBLY,

RECALLING Article 15(j) of the Convention on the International Maritime Organization concerning the functions of the Assembly in relation to regulations and guidelines concerning maritime safety,

RECALLING FURTHER that, by resolutions A.713(17) and A.797(19), it adopted measures to improve the safety of ships carrying solid bulk cargoes,

RECALLING ALSO that, in adopting resolution A.797(19), it requested the Maritime Safety Committee (MSC) to carry out, with high priority, its work on the safety of ships carrying solid bulk cargoes and to develop, as soon as possible, requirements and recommendations covering survivability standards, design and construction standards, management and training, operational standards, survey requirements and ship/shore interface aspects,

NOTING that, by resolution MSC.47(66), the MSC, at its sixty-sixth session, adopted amendments to the International Convention for the Safety of Life at Sea (SOLAS), 1974, to include a revised regulation 7 of chapter VI dealing with loading and unloading of bulk cargo,

NOTING FURTHER the approval by the MSC, at its sixty-sixth session, of MSC/Circ.743 on communications between maritime administrations and port authorities, whereby Governments in whose territories solid bulk cargo loading and unloading terminals are situated are invited to introduce port by-laws complying with operative paragraph 5 of that circular,

BEING CONCERNED at the continued loss of ships carrying solid bulk cargoes, sometimes without a trace, and the heavy loss of life incurred,

BEARING IN MIND that a number of accidents have occurred as a result of improper loading and unloading of bulk carriers and that the development of safe loading and unloading practices can prevent such accidents occurring in the future,

RECOGNIZING the need to improve the safe loading and unloading of bulk carriers,

RECOGNIZING FURTHER that such improvement could be achieved by the establishment of a composite code of practice for the safe loading and unloading of bulk carriers,

BELIEVING that the application of such a code of safe practice would enhance maritime safety,

HAVING CONSIDERED the recommendation made by the MSC at its sixty-sixth and sixty-eighth sessions,

1.   ADOPTS the Code of Practice for the Safe Loading and Unloading of Bulk Carriers, set out in the annex* to the present resolution;

2.   URGES Governments to implement this Code at the earliest possible opportunity and to inform IMO of any non-compliance;

3.   FURTHER URGES Governments in whose territories solid bulk cargo loading and unloading terminals are situated, to introduce port by-laws to the effect that:

   .1   terminal operators are required to comply with the relevant IMO codes and recommendations on ship/port co-operation;

   .2   terminal operators are required to appoint a "terminal representative" as stipulated in section 1.6 of the annex to resolution A.797(19);

   .3   the master is responsible at all times for the safe loading and unloading of the ship, the details of which should be confirmed with the terminal operator in the form of an agreed loading or unloading plan;

   .4   in case of non-compliance with the agreed loading or unloading plans or any other situation which endangers the safety of the ship, the master has the right to stop the loading or unloading; and

   .5   port authorities have the right to stop the loading or unloading of solid bulk cargoes when the safety of the ship carrying such cargoes is endangered.

4.   REQUESTS the MSC to keep this Code under review and to amend it, as necessary;

5.   REVOKES MSC/Circ.690 and DSC/Circ.3.

---

* See page 1.

MLD7

BLU Code

Code of Practice
for the Safe Loading and
Unloading of Bulk Carriers

Published in 1998 by the
INTERNATIONAL MARITIME ORGANIZATION
4 Albert Embankment, London SE1 7SR

Printed by the International Maritime Organization, London

6   8   10   9   7

ISBN 92-801-1458-1

IMO PUBLICATION
Sales number: I266E